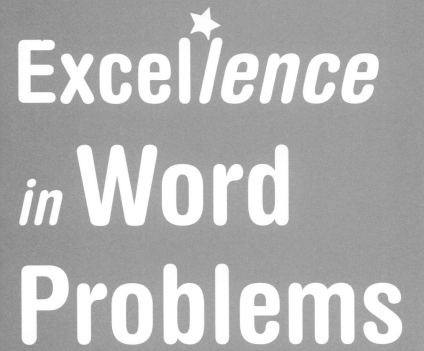

Excellence in Word Problems

Year **3**

By Karen Hamilton

RISING★STARS

Rising Stars UK Ltd., 76 Farnaby Road, Bromley,
BR1 4BH

Website: **www.risingstars-uk.com**

Every effort has been made to trace copyright
holders and obtain their permission for the use
of copyright material. The authors and
publishers will gladly receive information
enabling them to rectify any error or omission in
subsequent editions.

All facts are correct at time of going to press.

Published 2003
Reprinted 2004 (twice)
Text, design and layout ©Rising Stars UK Ltd.
Editorial: Tanya Solomons
Concept design: Burville Riley
Design: Ken Vail Graphic Design, Cambridge
Illustration copyright ©Louisa Burville-Riley
Cover photo ©Simon Battensby/Getty Images

British Library Cataloguing in Publication Data

A CIP record for this book is available from the
British Library.

ISBN 1-904591-19-1

Printed by Wyndeham Gait, Grimsby, UK

Contents

How to use this book

The *Excellence in Word Problems* series is designed to help you use your mathematical skills to solve a range a problems, many of which are written in words rather than figures.

Rather than giving a sum like:

4 × 6 =

a word problem might be along the lines of:

"If I have 4 six packs of cola, how many cans of cola do I have in total?"

The answer is the same, but you need to think about it a bit more and remember to answer by writing or saying: **"I have 24 cans of cola in total."**

The introduction

This section of each page gives you an idea of the sort of problems you are likely to see and helps you to understand what maths you need to use.

20   EXCELLENCE IN WORD PROBLEMS YEAR 3

Measures – capacity

Capacity problems might ask you to work out how many spoons or cups it would take to fill a large bottle or barrel. These are about dividing. You might also need to find out the difference between two capacities.

A glass has a capacity of 300 ml. Savanna drinks two glasses of water. How much water has she drunk altogether?

Read the question then read it again	Read slowly and carefully. Look at the numbers.
Choose your operations and units	How much... altogether? That's addition. The units here are ml (millilitres).
Estimate your answer	3 + 3 = 6. Add two '0' and I get 600. That seems right.
Calculate	300 ml + 300 ml = 600 ml. Savanna drank 600 ml of water.
Check your answer	Let's check using the inverse method. 600 – 300 = 300. Don't forget to put the units in. 600 ml.

Hints and tips
★ Capacity questions are going to be about these units:
    ml (millilitres)   cl (centilitres)   l (litres)

Hints and tips

The hints and tips section gives you useful ideas for completing the problems on the other page. These are the things you need to remember if you are doing a quiz or test!

The example problem

The flow chart takes you through an example problem *step-by-step*. This is important when answering word problems as it helps you to order your thoughts, do each part of the problem in the right order and *check your work*!

a) /vanna has a paddling pool with 10 l of water in it. If she empties /our litres, how much water is left in the paddling pool?

b) Savanna's dad drinks four cups of tea a day. Each cup holds 200 ml. How many millilitres of tea does he drink each day?

c) Savanna buys a 1 litre bottle of cola. Her sister Tyra has a can of cola with a capacity of 300 ml. How much more cola does the bottle hold than the can?

a) A jug has a capacity of $\frac{1}{2}$ l. Savanna needs to use the jug to fill a 6 l bucket. How many times does she need to fill the jug?

b) Savanna's mum drinks 6 mugs of tea a day. Each mug holds 300 ml. Savanna drinks two cups of tea a day. Each cup has a capacity of 200 ml. How much more tea does her mum drink than Savanna?

Challenge
Savanna has a 1 litre jug of lemonade. Help her to work out different ways of dividing the lemonade into two jugs. Example:　345 ml + 655 ml = 1000 ml

Every problem has the same five steps.
READ the question then read it again
CHOOSE your operations and units
ESTIMATE your answer
CALCULATE
CHECK your answer

We remember this by using this mnemonic:
RED
CLOWNS
ENTER
CAVES
CAREFULLY

The questions

The questions get harder as you go down the page.

- Section 1 questions are fairly straightforward and help you to practise your skills.
- Section 2 questions are a bit harder but will help you to remember all the key points.
- The Challenge sections are really tough and sometimes mean that you can make up games and your own questions! They can be great fun!

All about word problems

Ten top tips for working with word problems

1 *Work step-by-step*. Follow the flow chart.

Red	**R**ead the question then read it again
Clowns	**C**hoose your operations and units
Enter	**E**stimate your answer
Caves	**C**alculate
Carefully	**C**heck your answer

2 Always *show your working* or 'method'. This will help you to keep track of what you have done and may help you to get extra marks.

3 Always *include your units* in the answer. If you don't, you won't get full marks.

4   When you first read through a question, *underline important words and numbers*. This will help you to remember the important bits!

5   *Draw a picture* to help you. Sometimes a question is easier if you can 'see' it. Drawing 6 apples can help you if you need to divide them!

6   If the problem has a number of steps, break it down and do *one step at a time*.

7   When *checking your answers*, look at the inverse operation.

8   Sometimes an answer will 'sound right'. Read it out (quietly) and listen. *Does it make sense?*

9   If you are using measurements (grams, litres, cm), make sure that the *units are the same* before you calculate.

10   Once again! *Read the question then read it again.*

Place value

Place value questions often ask you to estimate a total or to do an operation with a number such as 10 or 100.

Help Jimmy to estimate these car mileages by rounding these numbers up or down to the nearest 10.

| 1 | 4 | 7 |

Read the question then read it again

Read slowly and carefully. This is about rounding up and down.

Choose your operations and units

I will need to round this one up. Remember to put 'miles' next to the answer.

Estimate your answer

I think it is rounding up. That will make it 150.

Calculate

147 rounded up to the nearest 10 is 150. My answer is 150.

Check your answer

Rounding down would give me 140. That is 7 from the number. 150 is just 3 from the number so I must be right.

Hints and tips

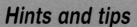 With place value it is important to remember **WHERE** the digits go. From left to right:

| 10,000s | 1000s | 100s | 10s | Units |

1

a) Help Jimmy to estimate these car mileages by rounding these numbers up or down to the nearest 10.

| 1 | 1 | 1 |

| 2 | 9 | 7 |

b) Show the mileage that would be 100 more than each of these:

| 4 | 5 | 3 |

| 3 | 4 | 1 | 6 |

c) Show the mileage that is 100 less than this:

| 2 | 2 | 4 | 0 |

2

a) At 7pm a television charity show has raised £7530. By 8pm they have raised £2000 more. How much have they raised so far?

b) By 9pm the audience have donated £11,050. How much more is needed to reach their £15,000 grand total?

Challenge

Choose four digits from 1 to 9.

How many different 4-digit numbers can be made? Try to work systematically.

Fractions

Problems about fractions usually ask you to find a fraction of a number or to work out what fraction a smaller number is of a bigger number.

Hannah has ten sweets. She eats half of them.
How many does she eat?

Read the question then read it again

Read slowly and carefully. Look at the numbers.

Choose your operations and units

Half is the same as 'divide by 2'. We need to give our answer in a number of sweets. I could use a number line too.

Estimate your answer

It should be about 5.

Calculate

10 sweets ÷ 2 = 5.
Hannah eats 5 sweets.

Check your answer

Check on the number line. Yes, there are 5 jumps on either side of 5, so 5 is half of 10.

Hints and tips

★ Drawing pictures can help with fractions.

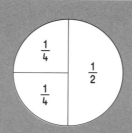

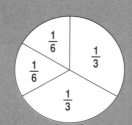

1

a) Hannah invites 16 children to her party. $\frac{1}{4}$ of them arrived by car and the rest walked. How many children came by car?

b) Hannah cuts her birthday cake into ten equal pieces. If she eats two pieces, what fraction of the cake is left?

c) How many more pieces does Hannah have to eat to have eaten half of the cake?

2

a) Hannah is going on a train journey. When she has travelled 60 kilometres she will have completed a third of the journey. How long is the total journey?

b) Hannah collects marbles. She has 100. She decides to give away one quarter of the total amount. How many does she have left?

Challenge

How many ways can you divide 24 without leaving a remainder?

Have a go at writing each calculation as a division sentence and a fraction statement.

Example: $24 \div 2 = 12$ and $\frac{1}{2}$ of 24 = 12

Addition and subtraction

Addition and subtraction questions can be about anything so remember to put in the unit or label next to each answer. This can be metres, litres or conkers!

Shannon is 7 years old. Her brother is three years older. How old is her brother?

Read the question then read it again

Read slowly and carefully. Look at the numbers – they are written out as words here.

Choose your operations and units

If her brother is older than Shannon we will have to add onto Shannon's age.

Estimate your answer

Her brother is more than 7 years old. But only 3 years older. That sounds like 10 to me!

Calculate

7 + 3 = 10

Check your answer

Check by reading the story aloud. 'Shannon's brother is 10 years old. That's 3 years older than 7.' I'm right!

Hints and tips

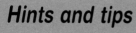 Reading your answer aloud when you have finished can help you to check your answer. It should 'sound' right to you!

1

a) Shannon has a sister who is 2 years younger than she is. How old is her sister?

b) Shannon's mum is 35. How old was she ten years ago?

c) Shannon is reading a book with 38 pages. She has read 12 pages so far.
How many more does she need to read to complete the book?

2

a) Shannon counts 67 cars in a car park. Five leave and another 19 arrive.
How many cars are there now?

b) Shannon collects football cards. She has bought 34.
Tyrell gives her 15 and her parents buy another 28 for her.
How many does she have in total?
How many more does she need to reach her 100 card goal?

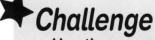 **Challenge**

Use three numbers and the + and – operations to make
different number sentences that total 20.

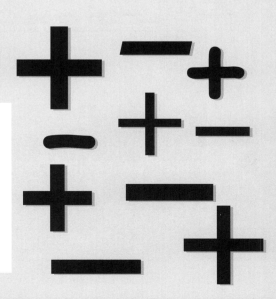

Money

Money questions can be adding, subtracting, multiplying or dividing. They also can be about giving or getting change for something.

Ajap buys one pencil for 40p. How much would two pencils cost?

Read the question then read it again

Read slowly and carefully. Look at the numbers.

Choose your operations and units

One pencil is 40p. I need to work out two lots of 40p. That's multiplying.

Estimate your answer

Two times 4 is 8. Add a '0' and I get 80. That should be it.

Calculate

40p × 2 = 80p
Two pencils would cost 80p.

Check your answer

I can check using addition.
40p + 40p = 80p

Hints and tips

★ Remember to put in the units on money questions:
  '£' for pounds   'p' for pence
     £3.50   or   86p

a) Ajay has 80p for a snack. He buys a pack of crisps for 40p and some chocolate for 35p. How much does he have left?

b) A child fare on the bus is 60p. How much does it cost for three children?

c) In his pocket Ajay has a 50p coin, two 20p coins and two 10p coins. How much does he have altogether?

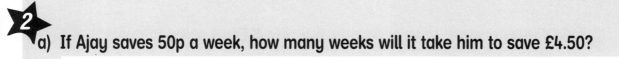

a) If Ajay saves 50p a week, how many weeks will it take him to save £4.50?

b) Ajay has been saving 20p every week. He has saved £2.40 so far. How many weeks has he been saving for?

c) Ajay has £10. He spends £4.75 on a football and £1.99 on a book. How much change does he get?

Challenge

£2.50 £1.90 £3.25 £1.75 £2.35 £1.10

Investigate which pairs of items you could buy for £5 or less.

Time

Time questions will have a start time and a finish time. You will need to work out either one or how long it is between the two different times.

Ben leaves his house at 8 o'clock to walk to school. It takes him 25 minutes. What time does he arrive?

Read the question then read it again	Read slowly and carefully. Look at the numbers. What are you being asked to do?
Choose your operations and units	Start at 8:00. Add 25 minutes. Remember to write out as a time.
Estimate your answer	25 minutes is nearly half an hour. It should be about 8:30 am.
Calculate	8:00 + 25 minutes = 8:25 am. Ben arrived at 8:25 am.
Check your answer	Use a clock face to help you.

Hints and tips

★ You can use a clock face to help you with these questions. Remember there are only 60 minutes in an hour so each time you go past 59 in minutes you must add another hour!

1

a) Ben arrives at school at 8:25 and he plays for 20 minutes before going into his class. What time does he go to class?

b) Ben puts cookies in the oven at 9:30 am. He takes them out at 9:55. How long were they in the oven?

c) Lunchtime starts at quarter past 12. It lasts for 50 minutes. What time does lunchtime end?

2

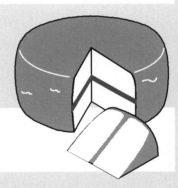

a) Ben takes a chocolate cake out of the oven at 2:30. It took 1 hour and 20 minutes to bake. What time did he put it in?

b) Ben watches a film that lasts for 1 hour and 30 minutes. It starts at 7:15. What time will it finish?

Challenge

Write down six pairs of times with a time interval of 40 minutes.

Measures – length

Length questions can be about very short lengths (mm) or huge lengths (miles or km). The problems may be about a journey or measuring something in your home.

Yunus has two pieces of string 9 cm long and 8 cm long. What is the difference in their lengths?

Read the question then read it again

Read slowly and carefully. Look at the numbers.

Choose your operations and units

I have to find the 'difference'. That's subtraction! The units are cm (centimetres).

Estimate your answer

9 and 8 are pretty close so the answer will be very small, say 1.

Calculate

9 – 8 = 1. Include the units. The difference in length is 1cm.

Check your answer

I can check using the inverse. 8 cm + 1 cm = 9 cm. I'm right!

Hints and tips

★ Length questions are going to be about these units:

mm (millimetres)   cm (centimetres)   m (metres)   km (kilometres)

You might also be asked to use miles. A mile is about 1.6 kilometres.

1

a) Yunus has the same pieces of string. One is 9cm and the other 8cm.
What is their total length?

b) Yunus cuts a piece of ribbon into four equal pieces. Each new piece is
20cm long. How long was the original piece of ribbon?

c) On Sports Day, Yunus jumps 110cm in the sandpit. Jason jumps 85cm.
How much further does Yunus jump?

2

a) The wall in the shady area of the playground is 10m long. New benches
are 1.5m long. How many benches could be placed along the wall?

b) Yunus' mum buys 6m of fencing for the back of the garden. She needs to go
back to the garden centre to buy 2 more metres. How wide is their back garden?

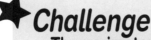**Challenge**

The perimeter of a rectangular garden is 30 metres.
The perimeter is the measurement all the way around
the outside of a shape.
What could each side of the garden measure?
Suggest two different sets of measurements.

Measures – capacity

Capacity problems might ask you to work out how many spoons or cups it would take to fill a large bottle or barrel. These are about dividing. You might also need to find out the difference between two capacities.

A glass has a capacity of 300 ml. Savanna drinks two glasses of water. How much water has she drunk altogether?

Read the question then read it again	Read slowly and carefully. Look at the numbers.
Choose your operations and units	How much... altogether? That's addition. The units here are ml (millilitres).
Estimate your answer	3 + 3 = 6. Add two '0' and I get 600. That seems right.
Calculate	300 ml + 300 ml = 600 ml Savanna drank 600 ml of water.
Check your answer	Let's check using the inverse method. 600 – 300 = 300. Don't forget to put the units in. 600 ml.

Hints and tips

★ Capacity questions are going to be about these units:

   ml (millilitres)   cl (centilitres)   l (litres)

1

a) Savanna has a paddling pool with 10 l of water in it. If she empties
four litres, how much water is left in the paddling pool?

b) Savanna's dad drinks four cups of tea a day. Each cup holds 200 ml.
How many millilitres of tea does he drink each day?

c) Savanna buys a 1 litre bottle of cola. Her sister Tyra has a can of cola with
a capacity of 300 ml. How much more cola does the bottle hold than the can?

2

a) A jug has a capacity of $\frac{1}{2}$ l. Savanna needs to use the jug to fill a 6 l bucket.
How many times does she need to fill the jug?

b) Savanna's mum drinks 6 mugs of tea a day.
Each mug holds 300 ml. Savanna drinks two cups of tea a day. Each cup has
a capacity of 200 ml. How much more tea does her mum drink than Savanna?

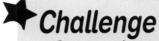

Challenge

Savanna has a 1 litre jug of lemonade.
Help her to work out different ways of dividing the lemonade into two jugs.
Example: 345 ml + 655 ml = 1000 ml

Measures – mass

Problems about mass can either be longer 'story' type problems, which need careful thinking about, or shorter calculations questions. Remember to always put in the units (g, kg).

One packet of mints weighs 20g. How much do four packets weigh?

Read the question then read it again	Read slowly and carefully. Look at the numbers. What are you being asked to do with them?
Choose your operations and units	Four packets of mints. That sounds like multiplication. Don't forget the units. That's g for grams!
Estimate your answer	$4 \times 2 = 8$. That should be about 80g when we add the '0'.
Calculate	20 grams $\times$ 4 = 80 grams. Four packets of mints weigh 80g.
Check your answer	Let's try to check by 'repeated addition'. $20 + 20 + 20 + 20 = 80$. Remember the units. That's 80g!

Hints and tips

★ Capacity questions are going to be about these units:
g (grams)   kg (kilograms)
Use what you know to work out harder facts. To multiply by four, it is easier to double and double again!

1

a) Ellie has lost two packets of her mints. She now has two packets each weighing 20g. How much do these weigh together? Can you answer this question using two different methods?

b) Ellie has three packets of Chewy Chomps. They weigh 60g altogether. How much does one packet weigh?

c) Ellie has two parcels with a total weight of 1 kilogram. She knows that one parcel weighs 450g. How much does the other parcel weigh?

2

SHORTBREAD COOKIES
(Ingredients to make 10 cookies)
 150g plain flour
  90g butter or margarine
  50g caster sugar

a) Help Ellie to work out how much 10 shortbread cookies weigh.

b) Ellie wants to make 30 cookies. How much of each ingredient would she need?

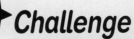 *Challenge*

Ellie has three toys in a sack. They weigh 1kg altogether.
How much could each toy weigh? Write down at least 10 different combinations.

Puzzles

Number puzzles sometimes ask you to look for patterns. They also ask you to find numbers when you know something about each one, e.g. the sum when they are added and the product when they are multiplied.

When I multiply my number by 2, I get 12. What is my number?

Read the question then read it again

Read slowly and carefully. Look at the numbers. I need to find 'my number'.

Choose your operations and units

The opposite (or inverse) of multiplication is division. So, if I divide 12 by 2, I should get my number.

Estimate your answer

I think it should be 6.

Calculate

12 ÷ 2 = 6
My number is 6.

Check your answer

Check by changing 'my number' for 6. Yes, I'm right!

Hints and tips

★ Use the **INVERSE** number operation to work out the missing number.
Addition and subtraction are inverse operations.
Multiplication and division are inverse operations.

1

a) When I multiply my number by 8, I get 16. What is my number?

b) When I add 19 to my number, I get 42. What's my number?

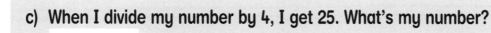

+ 19 = 42

c) When I divide my number by 4, I get 25. What's my number?

÷ 4 = 25

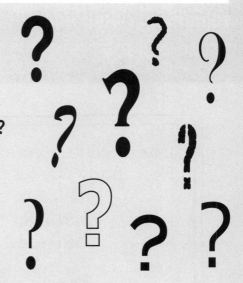

2

a) When I add 10 to my number then halve the answer I get 10.
What's my number?

b) When I divide my number by 4 then add 9, I get 34.
What's my number?

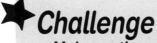

★ Challenge

Make up three number puzzles and give them to a friend to work out.

1	2	3

Multiplication and division

Multiplication and division problems are often set in the kitchen where you have to divide or multiply ingredients. Remember your times tables here!

Daniel collects comics. He buys two every week for three weeks. How many comics does he have after three weeks?

Read the question then read it again

Read slowly and carefully. Think about the numbers. What are you being asked to do?

Choose your operations and units

Two comics... for 3 weeks. That sounds like multiplication to me.

Estimate your answer

Well, I know that 2 × 3 is 6, so it must be 6 comics.

Calculate

2 × 3 = 6
Daniel has 6 comics.

Check your answer

Check by adding.
2 comics + 2 comics + 2 comics = 6 comics. Yes!

Hints and tips

★ You can check multiplication and division by doing the OPPOSITE sum. For multiplication, use division to check. For division, use multiplication to check.

1

a) Daniel gets 4 packs of 6 football stickers. How many stickers does he have altogether?

b) Daniel is having a birthday party. He has invited nine children. He will give each child a goody-bag containing ten marbles. How many marbles will he give away in total?

c) Daniel's teacher has asked him to arrange forty chairs in five equal rows in the hall. How many chairs will there be in each row?

2

a) Which number sentence shows how to work out how many chairs there will be in each row?

$5 \div 40$ $40 + 5$ 5×40 $40 \div 5$

b) Daniel is handing out pencils. They come in packs of five. He has seven packets of pencils. Does he have enough to give one pencil to each of the twenty-four children in his class?

c) Daniel has 6 sweets and his sister Marcia has 6 sweets. Karen has no sweets. All the sweets are shared between the three children. How many sweets does each child get?

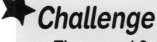 **Challenge**

There are 48 children taking part in a marble tournament. How many ways can they be divided into teams of equal size?

Position and direction

Position and direction questions can be about compass directions or finding a point on a grid. The problems can also be about horizontal or vertical lines.

Christopher is facing north. He turns clockwise through one right angle. Which direction is he facing now?

Read the question then read it again

Read slowly and carefully. Remember that clockwise is to the right!

Choose your operations and units

I need to find a direction on the compass point, so it will be north, south, east or west.

Estimate your answer

The next one to north is east when I go right so I will try that one.

Calculate

I start facing north and move a right angle (that's 90 degrees) clockwise (that's to the right). 90 degrees is $\frac{1}{4}$ turn, so it must be east! Christopher is facing east.

Check your answer

Check that you have moved clockwise and just one $\frac{1}{4}$ turn.

W $\overset{N}{\underset{S}{}}$ E

Hints and tips

★ Draw a compass on a piece of card. Attach an arrow to the centre. Move the arrow as you follow the instructions.

★ Clockwise

★ Remember the points of a compass like this:
Never **E**at **S**hredded **W**heat
North **E**ast **S**outh **W**est

1

a) Christopher is facing south. He turns clockwise through two right angles. Which direction is he facing now?

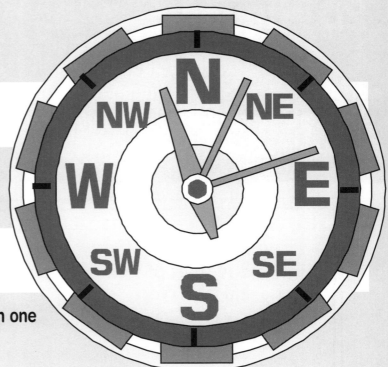

b) Christopher is facing west. He turns anti-clockwise through two right angles. Which direction is he facing now?

c) Christopher has turned clockwise through one right angle. He is now facing south. Where did he start?

2

a) Christopher turns clockwise through half a right angle. He is now facing north. Where did he start?

b) Christopher is facing south west (SW). He has turned clockwise through one right angle and then anti-clockwise through two right angles. Where did he start?

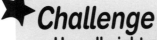 *Challenge*

Use all eight compass points and write instructions for a partner to follow.

Useful words: clockwise   anti-clockwise   turn   right angle   north   south   east   west

2D shapes

Questions about 2D shapes often ask you to talk about their properties (number of sides, whether sides are equal or parallel). Some problems will need you to draw shapes as well.

How many lines of symmetry does a square have?

Read the question then read it again

Read slowly and carefully. This question is about symmetry.

Choose your operations and units

Symmetry is about mirror lines. Where can I draw them?

Estimate your answer

I think there will be about 4 lines of symmetry.

Calculate

Draw the lines in. Are both sides equal?

Check your answer

My drawing shows 4 lines. I must be right.

Hints and tips

★ Remember the key things about shapes:
   a) Number of sides.
   b) Are sides parallel?
   c) Are there right angles?

★ Drawing shapes can help you to 'see' the answers.

1

a) How many lines of symmetry does a rectangle have?

b) Name three polygons that have two pairs of parallel lines.

c) Sort these polygons into the Carroll diagram below.

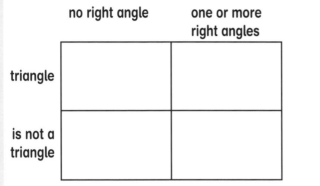

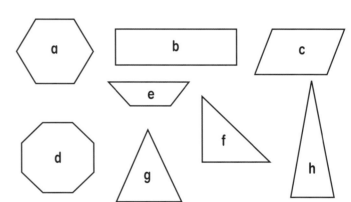

2

a) Draw a shape that has four sides and two right angles.

b) Draw a shape with two parallel sides and only ONE right angle.

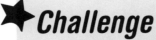

Challenge

On a separate piece of paper, draw as many different rectangles as you can with a **PERIMETER** of 24 cm. Remember, perimeter means the distance **ALL AROUND** a shape.

3D shapes

Problems about 3D shapes will often ask you to work out how many faces, edges and vertices there are. You might also be asked how many smaller shapes fit into a bigger one.

Shan's baby brother builds a tower of cubes.
How many faces are touching each other?

Read the question then read it again

Read slowly and carefully. This question is about 'faces'.

Choose your operations and units

There are 6 cubes. I have to work out how many are touching.

Estimate your answer

I think there will be more than 6 faces touching each other.

Calculate

Working methodically, two at the top, two further down and so on... There are 10 faces touching each other.

Check your answer

Check again. Yes, there are 10 faces touching each other.

Hints and tips

★ When thinking about 3D shapes, remember that you are looking for the number of 'faces' and number of 'sides'.

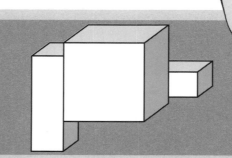

Shan makes a shape out of cubes and describes it to a friend.

My shape is made using 6 cubes.
The tallest part is two cubes high. The base makes an L shape.
The arms of the L are the same length.
The tower is in the corner of the L.

1

What is the least number of cubes that Shan would need to build this shape?
Have a go at making Shan's shape.

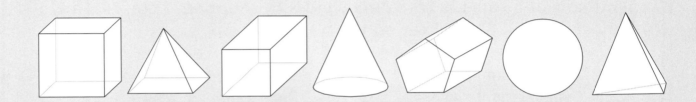

2

a) Shan chooses two different polyhedrons. They have 16 edges in total.
    Which two shapes could they be?

b) Shan chooses three shapes that have a total of more than 15 faces.
    Which three polyhedrons could it be? Give at least two different combinations.

 **Challenge**

Play *What am I?* with a partner.
EXAMPLE : "I have 6 faces. I have 8 vertices and 12 edges. My faces are square.
           What am I?"
Take it in turns to make up clues for each other.
Score a point each time you guess correctly.
Have three turns each.

Two-step problems

Two-step problems have two steps! It is important to work out what each step is asking you to do before you complete it.

Chanel is walking to school with 18 grapes. She gives 6 away to her friend Jane and eats the rest. Finley gives her another 4 grapes. How many grapes did Chanel eat on the way to school.

Read the question then read it again

> This is a step-by-step question. Read it through slowly.

Choose your operations and units

> I need to take away first, then add.

Estimate your answer

> I think she ate fewer than she took to school, say 16.

Calculate

> 18 – 6 = 12. She ate 12 of her own grapes.
> 12 + 4 = 16. Her own grapes + Finley's makes 16.
> Chanel ate 16 grapes.

Check your answer

> Do the inverse to check.
> 16 – 4 = 12
> 12 + 6 = 18. Yes! I was right!

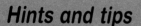

Hints and tips

★ Always work step-by-step when working on two-step problems. Keep notes of everything you have done so you don't get lost. Draw pictures if it helps you to get the right answer!

a) Chanel counts 35 people on the bus. 9 get off and 3 get on.
How many people are on the bus now?

b) Chanel collects sheets of stickers. She has two sheets with 8 stickers and
four sheets with 10 stickers. How many stickers does she have altogether?

c) Chanel's class have collected £20 for charity. Their head teacher says that
she will give double the amount the children have collected. What is the total
amount they give to charity?

a) All 340 children in the school vote about having a longer morning playtime.
A quarter of them vote NO, the rest vote YES. How many children want a
longer playtime?

b) Cathy has forgotten to list the price of a drink.
How much would it cost to buy a drink on its own?

Cathy's Café	
Sandwich and drink	£1.20
Sandwich	65 p
Slice of cake	90 p
Soup of the day	£1.10

Challenge

Make up a word problem for each of these number sentences.
Use your friends' names in the problem.

100 – 20 + 10 =

(2 × 10) – 5 =

Data handling

Problems involving data handling often mean you have to accurately read graphs, charts and tables.

Jered asked his classmates what their favourite flavour of ice-cream is.

What is the least popular flavour?

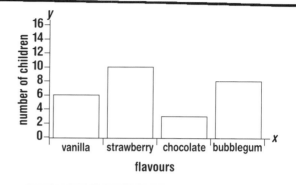

Read the question then read it again

I need to look at this bar chart and answer questions.

Choose your operations and units

I am looking for the lowest bar on the chart. Then I need to work out how many.

Estimate your answer

I think it's going to be chocolate.

Calculate

3 people liked chocolate, 6 liked vanilla, 8 liked bubblegum and 10 strawberry. Chocolate must be right! Chocolate was the least popular flavour.

Check your answer

Check again. The lowest bar is for chocolate, I must be right!

Hints and tips

★ When looking at charts and graphs, look at the names of the x axis (side to side) and the y axis (up and down). These will tell you what the chart is about.

★ Read carefully. Use a ruler if you need to draw a chart or graph.

1

Use the chart on page 36 to answer these questions about ice cream!

a) Which was the most popular flavour?

b) How many more children liked strawberry than chocolate?

c) How many children did Jered ask?

2

Jered surveyed some friends. Here are his results.

	boy	not a boy
8 years old	Will Remelle	Steph Julia
not 8 years	Solkan Jimmy Ajay	Asweeni Shanice Stacey Shannon Emine

a) How many of the children are boys?

b) How many of the girls are not 8 years old?

★ *Challenge*

Use a blank Carroll diagram like this one to collect data about 10 of your classmates. You will need to decide on two categories of information, such as age, eye colour, favourite colour or gender.

	brown eyes	not brown eyes
girl		
not a girl		

Patterns

Problems involving patterns and sequences usually need you to work out the differences between the numbers.

This is a pattern.   3, 6, 9, 12, 15, ___, ___, ___

Add in the next three numbers and write the rule.

Read the question then read it again

Careful here. There are two parts to this question.

Choose your operations and units

The numbers are going up. This is an adding pattern.
I will need to subtract to find the pattern though.

Estimate your answer

I think it's adding in 3s.

Calculate

15 – 12 = 3, 6 – 3 = 3. Yes the pattern is 3s, so the next three numbers are 15 + 3 = 18, 18 + 3 = 21, 21 + 3 = 24.
The next three numbers are 18, 21 and 24. The rule is 'add 3 to find the next number'.

Check your answer

Check again by subtraction. Yes, I'm right!

Hints and tips

★ With patterns, use the numbers you already have to work out the pattern first. This will make finding the answers easy.

★ Work step-by-step with patterns and write down your method.

1

Write the next three numbers in each sequence and write the rule.

a) 8, 10, 12, 14, ___, ___, ___

b) 24, 21, 18, 15, ___, ___, ___

c) 35, 30, 25, 20, ___, ___, ___

2

a) Write the three numbers that come **BEFORE** the first number in this sequence.
___, ___, ___, 35, 39, 43, 47

b) Complete this sequence. Describe any pattern you see.
___, ___, 14, 19, 24, ___, 34 ___

c) Complete this sequence. Describe any pattern you see.
6, 16, ___, 36, ___, ___, ___

★ Challenge

Make up a number sequence that stops at 30.

Decide whether the numbers will increase or decrease.
Ask a friend to have a go at describing any patterns
that they can see.

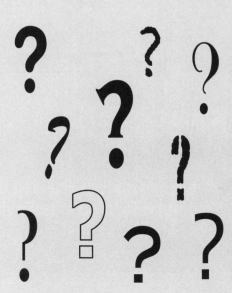

Decimals

Problems about decimals are usually word stories. Many are about money and sometimes you will have to convert between pounds and pence. Remember to always put the decimal point in!

Roshanne saves £3.50 and is given £5 for her birthday. How much more does she need to save to be able to buy a CD worth £10?

Read the question then read it again

This is about money. How much more does she need to save? This is a subtraction sum, I think.

Choose your operations and units

This is subtraction... but first I have to add the money she does have.

Estimate your answer

I think the answer will be between £1 and £2.

Calculate

Roshanne has £3.50 and £5. £3.50 + £5 = £8.50. She needs £10. £10.00 − £8.50 = £1.50 Roshanne needs to save £1.50.

Check your answer

Check again by subtraction, yes I'm right!

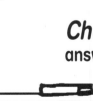

Hints and tips

★ When you are working with decimals, it is important to put the decimal point in the right place.

£1.10 £2.75 £3.90

£2.50 £1.25 £3.40

1

a) Roshanne buys a yo-yo and a packet of pencils. How much does she spend?

b) Roshanne has saved £1.50. She wants to buy a teddy bear. How much more does she need to save?

c) Which two items can be bought for exactly £5?

2

a) Roshanne's books weigh 1.5 kilograms. Mya's books weigh 800 grams less. How much do Mya's books weigh?

b) Roshanne has three pieces of string, 1.5m, 60cm and 2.8m. What is their total length?

Challenge

Roshanne buys one of each item in the shop above and gets 10p change. How much money did she give the shop keeper?

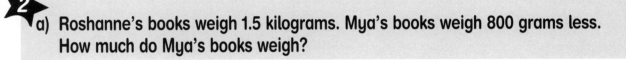

Mixed bag

These questions could be about anything! Read them carefully so you understand what you are being asked to do.

Theo and his friend Dan have eaten 5 hot dogs between them. They now each eat another 2 hot dogs. How many hot dogs have they eaten altogether?

Read the question then read it again

OK. 'How many altogether?' This is addition.

Choose your operations and units

I have to add the first number to 2... and another 2.

Estimate your answer

I think it will be about 9.

Calculate

5 hot dogs + 2 hot dogs + 2 hot dogs = 9 hot dogs.
They have eaten 9 hot dogs.

Check your answer

Check again by subtraction. Yes, I'm right!

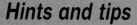

Hints and tips

★ When answering mixed questions, follow the steps carefully. Think about the units and the operations you will need to use. If you get this right, you won't go wrong!

 1

a) Today is Monday 16th March. What date will it be in 10 days?

b) Emine walks 1.5 km. Theo walks twice as far. How far does Theo walk?

c) What change would Theo get from £5 if he spends £3.47?

 2

a) If 4 bouncy balls cost £6, how much do 3 balls cost?

b) A pen costs 20p. How many could Emine buy for £4.20?

 ## Challenge

There are 48 pages in this book. There are 18 pages of questions and 18 pages of notes to help you. How many pages does that leave?

Answers

Place value

a) 110 and 300
b) 553 and 3516
c) 2140

a) £9530
b) £3950

Challenge
Answers will vary.

Fractions

a) 4
b) $\frac{8}{10}$ or $\frac{4}{5}$
c) 3 pieces

a) 180 km
b) 75 marbles

Challenge

$24 \div 1 = 24$ or $\frac{1}{1}$ of $24 = 24$

$24 \div 3 = 8$ or $\frac{1}{3}$ of $24 = 8$

$24 \div 4 = 6$ or $\frac{1}{4}$ of $24 = 6$

$24 \div 6 = 4$ or $\frac{1}{6}$ of $24 = 4$

$24 \div 8 = 3$ or $\frac{1}{8}$ of $24 = 3$

Addition and subtraction

a) 5 years old
b) 25 years old
c) 26 pages

a) 81 cars
b) 77 cards. 23 needed for 100 card goal.

Challenge
Answers will vary but should add to 20.

Money

a) 5p
b) £1.80
c) £1.10

a) 9 weeks
b) 12 weeks
c) £3.26

Challenge
Answers will vary but could include:
Spinner and pen, yo-yo, skipping rope or toy car.
Fountain pen and yo-yo, skipping rope, toy car.
Football and skipping rope or yo-yo.
Yo-yo and skipping rope or toy car.
Skipping rope and toy car.

Time

a) 8:45
b) 25 minutes
c) 13:05 or 1:05

a) 1:10
b) 8:45

Challenge
Answers will vary but there must be an interval of 40 minutes between each time.

Measures – length

a) 17 cm
b) 80 cm
c) 25 cm

a) 6 benches
b) 8 m

Challenge
Measurements could be 10m + 10m + 5m + 5m.
or 9m + 9m + 6m + 6m Totals should add up to 30m.

Measures – capacity

a) 6 l
b) 800 ml
c) 700 ml

a) 12 times
b) 1.4 l

Challenge
Answers will vary but totals should equal 1000 ml or 1 l.

Measures – mass

a) 40 g. You could add 20g + 20g or multiply
   20g × 2 to get the answer.
b) 20 g
c) 550 g

a) 290 g
b) 450g plain flour, 270g butter, 150g caster sugar

Challenge
Answers will vary.

Puzzles

a) 2
b) 23
c) 100

a) 10
b) 100

Challenge
Answers will vary.

Multiplication and division

a) 24 stickers
b) 90 marbles
c) 8 chairs in each row

a) Tick the last box
b) Yes because there are 35 pencils in total:
   7 × 5 = 35
c) 4 sweets

Challenge
2 teams of 24, 3 teams of 16, 4 teams of 12,
6 teams of 8, 8 teams of 6, 12 teams of 4,
16 teams of 3 or 24 teams of 2!

Position and direction

a) North
b) East
c) West

a) North east
b) South east

Challenge
Answers will vary.

2D shapes

a) 2
b) Square, Rectangle, Hexagon, Octagon, Rhombus

	no right angle	one or more right angles
triangle	g, h	f
is not a triangle	a, c, d, e	b

a) Answers will vary.
b) Answers will vary.

Challenge
Answers will vary.

3D shapes

6 cubes
Check shape against picture

a) Pentagonal prism and cone
b) There are many possible combinations, for
   example: cube, square-based pyramid and
   pentagonal prism; cube, cuboid and triangular
   pyramid.

Challenge
Cube. Children's answers will vary.

Two-step problems

a) 29
b) 56 stickers
c) £60

a) 255 vote YES!
b) 55p

Challenge
Answers will vary.

Data handling

a) Strawberry
b) 7
c) 27 children

a) 5 boys
b) 5

Challenge
Answers will vary.

Patterns

a) 8, 10, 12, 14, **16**, **18**, **20** Add 2
b) 24, 21, 18, 15, **12**, 9, 6 Take away 3
c) 35, 30, 25, 20, **15**, **10**, **5** Take away 5

a) 23, 27, **31**, 35, 39, 43, 37 Add 4
b) 4, 9, 14, 19, 24, 29, 34, **39** Add 5
c) 6, 16, **26**, 36, **46**, 56, **66** Add 10

Challenge
Answers will vary.

Decimals

a) £3.60
b) £1.90
c) Pencil and football

a) 700 g
b) 4.9 m

Challenge
£15.00

Mixed bag

a) Thursday 26th March
b) 3 km
c) £1.53

a) £4.50
b) 21 pens

Challenge
12 pages

Your notes